Young Lions

Song of the City

Well, some people like suburban life
Some people like the sea
Others like the countryside
But . . . it's the city life
For me.

These poems will take you dancing through the city, and show you ordinary things from extraordinary angles. You'll meet all too familiar people like bossy Queen Eileen, or yawn sympathetically through Miss Creedle's Creative Writing class. Some poems will take you round familiar-sounding streets and sights: others will unexpectedly lift you into the realms of the unknown.

Observant and original, their appeal is irresistible; and Jonathan Hills's imaginative, individual line drawings illustrate them beautifully.

Other books by Gareth Owen

Salford Road and other poems
Douglas the Drummer

for older readers

Never Walk Alone
The Man With Eyes Like Windows

Gareth Owen

Song of the City

Illustrated by Jonathan Hills

Young Lions
An Imprint of HarperCollinsPublishers

First published in Young Lions 1985
Fifth impression February 1992

Young Lions is an imprint of the Children's Division,
part of HarperCollins Publishers Ltd,
77–85 Fulham Palace Road, Hammersmith,
London W6 8JB

Text copyright © Gareth Owen 1985
Illustrations copyright © Jonathan Hills 1985

ISBN 0-00-672410-8

Printed and bound in Great Britain by
HarperCollins Manufacturing, Glasgow

Contents

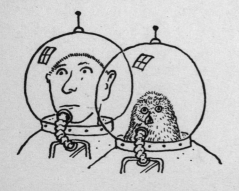

The Owl and the Astronaut

The owl and the astronaut
Sailed through space
In their intergalactic ship
They kept hunger at bay
With three pills a day
And drank through a protein drip.
The owl dreamed of mince
And slices of quince
And remarked how life had gone flat;
'It may be all right
To fly faster than light
But I preferred the boat and the cat.'

Thoughts like an Ocean

The sea comes to me on the shore
On lacy slippered feet
And shyly, slyly slides away
With a murmur of defeat.

And as I stand there wondering
Strange thoughts spin round my head
Of why and where and what and when
And if not, why, what then?

Where do lobsters come from?
And where anemones?
And are there other worlds out there
With other mysteries?

Why do *I* walk upon dry land
While fishes haunt the sea?
And as I think about their lives
Do they too think of me?

Why is water, water?
Why does it wet my hand?
Are there really as many stars
As there are grains of sand?

And where would the ocean go to
If there were no gravity?
And where was I before I lived?
And where's eternity?

Perhaps the beach I'm standing on
Perhaps this stretch of sand
Perhaps the Universe itself
Lies on someone else's hand?

And isn't it strange how this water and I
At this moment happencd to meet
And how this tide sweeps half the world
Before stopping at my feet.

Come on in the Water's Lovely

Come on in the water's lovely
It isn't really cold at all
Of course you'll be quite safe up this end
If you hold tight to the wall.

Of course that fat boy there won't drown you
He's too busy drowning Gail
Just imagine you're a tadpole.
I *know* you haven't got a tail.

Oh come on in the water's lovely
Warm and clear as anything
All the bottom tiles are squiggly
And your legs like wriggly string.

Come on in the water's lovely
It's no good freezing on the side
How do you know you're going to drown
Unless you've really tried.

What? You're really going to do it?
You'll jump in on the count of three?
Of course the chlorine doesn't blind you
Dive straight in and you'll soon see.

One – it isn't really deep at all.
Two – see just comes to my chin.
Three – oh there's the bell for closing time
And just as you jumped in!

TYPEWRITING CLASS

Dear Miss Hinson
I am spitting
In front of my top ratter
With the rest of my commercesnail sturdy students
Triping you this later.
The truce is Miss Hinson
I am not hippy wiht my cross.
Every day on Woundsday
I sit in my dusk
With my type rutter
Trooping without lurking at the lattice
All sorts of weird messengers.
To give one exam pill,
'The quick down socks.....
The quick brine pox.....
The sick frown box....
The sick down jocks
Humps over the hazy bog'
When everyone kows
That a sick down jock
Would not be seen dead
Near a hazy bog.
Another one we tripe is;
'Now is the tame
For all guide men
To cram to the head
Of the pratty.'
To may why of sinking
I that is all you get to tripe
In true whelks of sturdy
Then I am thinking of changing
To crookery classes.
I would sooner end up a crook
Than a shirt hand trappist
Any die of the wink.
I have taken the tremble, Miss Hinson
To trip you this later
So that you will be able
To understand my indignation.
I must clothe now
As the Bill is groaning   Yours fitfully.....

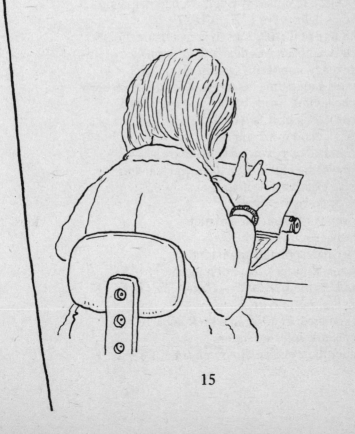

Miss Creedle Teaches
Creative Writing

'This morning,' cries Miss Creedle,
'We're all going to use our imaginations,
We're going to close our eyes 3W and imagine.
Are we ready to imagine Darren?
I'm going to count to three.
At one, we wipe our brains completely clean;
At two, we close our eyes;
And at three, we imagine.
Are we all imagining? Good.
Here is a piece of music by Beethoven to help us.
Beethoven's dates were 1770 to 1827.
(See The Age of Revolutions in your History books.)
Although Beethoven was deaf and a German
He wrote many wonderful symphonies,
But this was a long time before anyone of us was born.
Are you imagining a time before you were born?
What does it look like? Is it dark?
(Embryo is a good word you might use.)
Does the music carry you away like a river?
What is the name of the river? Can you smell it?
Foetid is an exciting adjective.
As you float down the river
Perhaps you land on an alien planet.
Tell me what sounds you hear.
If there are indescribable monsters
Tell me what they look like but not now.
(Your book entitled *Tackle Pre-History This Way*
Will be of assistance here.)
Perhaps you are cast adrift in a broken barrel.
In stormy shark-infested waters
(Remember the work we did on piranhas for R.E.?)

Try to see yourself. Can you do that?
See yourself at the bottom of a pothole in the Andes
With both legs broken
And your life ebbing away inexorably.
What does the limestone feel like?
See the colours.
Have you done that? Good.
And now you may open your eyes.
Your imagining time is over,
Now it is writing time.
Are we ready to write? Good.
Then write away.
Wayne, you're getting some exciting ideas down.
Tracy, that's lovely.
Darren, you haven't written anything.
Couldn't you put the date?
You can't think of anything to write.
Well, what did you see when you closed your eyes?
But you must have seen something beside the black.
Yes, apart from the little squiggles.
Just the black. I see.
Well, try to think
Of as many words for black as you can.'

Miss Creedle whirls about the class
Like a benign typhoon
Spinning from one quailing homestead to another.
I dream of peaceful ancient days
In Mr Swindell's class
When the hours passed like a dream
Filled with order and measuring and tests.

17

Excitement is not one of the things I come to school for.
I force my eyes shut
Kicking ineffectually at the starter;
But all I see
Is a boy of twelve
Sitting at a desk one dark November day
Writing this poem.
And Darren is happy to discover
There is only one word for black
And that will have to suffice
Until the bell rings for all of us.

Out in the City

When you're out in the city
Shuffling down the street,
A bouncy city rhythm
Starts to boogie in your feet.

It jumps off the pavement,
There's a snare drum in your brain,
It pumps through your heart
Like a diesel train.

There's Harry on the corner,
Sings, 'How she goin' boy?'
To loose and easy Winston
With his brother Leroy.

Shout, 'Hello!' to Billy Brisket
With his tripes and cows heels,
Blood-stained rabbits
And trays of live eels.

Maltese Tony
Smoking in the shade
Keeping one good eye
On the amusement arcade.

And everybody's talking:

Move along
Step this way
Here's a bargain
What you say?
Mind your backs
Here's your stop
More fares?
Room on top.

Neon lights and take-aways
Gangs of boys and girls
Football crowds and market stalls
Taxi cabs and noise.

From the city cafes
On the smoky breeze
Smells of Indian cooking
Greek and Cantonese.

Well, some people like suburban life
Some people like the sea
Others like the countryside
But it's the city
Yes it's the city
It's the city life
For me.

The Commentator

Good afternoon and welcome
To this international
Between England and Holland
Which is being played here today
At 4, Florence Terrace.
And the pitch looks in superb condition
As Danny Markey, the England captain,
Puts England on the attack.
Straight away it's Markey
With a lovely little pass to Keegan,
Keegan back to Markey,
Markey in possession here
Jinking skilfully past the dustbins;
And a neat flick inside the cat there.
What a brilliant player this Markey is
And he's still only nine years old!
Markey to Francis,
Francis back to Markey,
Markey is through, he's through,
No, he's been tackled by the drainpipe;
But he's won the ball back brilliantly
And he's advancing on the Dutch keeper,
It must be a goal.
The keeper's off his line
But Markey chips him superbly
And it's a goal
No!

It's gone into Mrs Spence's next door.
And Markey's going round to ask for his ball back,
It could be the end of this international.
Now the door's opening
And yes, it's Mrs Spence,
Mrs Spence has come to the door.
Wait a minute
She's shaking her head, she is shaking her head,
She's not going to let England have their ball back.
What is the referee going to do?
Markey's coming back looking very dejected,
And he seems to be waiting . . .
He's going back,
Markey is going back for that ball!
What a brilliant and exciting move!
He waited until the front door was closed
And then went back for that ball.
And wait a minute,
He's found it, Markey has found that ball,
He has found that ball
And that's wonderful news
For the hundred thousand fans gathered here
Who are showing their appreciation
In no uncertain fashion.
But wait a minute,
The door's opening once more.
It's her, it's Mrs Spence
And she's waving her fist
And shouting something I can't quite understand
But I don't think it's encouragement.
And Markey's off,
He's jinked past her on the outside

Dodging this way and that
With Mrs Spence in hot pursuit.
And he's past her, he's through,
What skills this boy has!
But Mr Spence is there too,
Mr Spence in the sweeper role
With Rover their dog.
Markey's going to have to pull out all the stops now.
He's running straight at him,
And he's down, he's down on all fours!
What is he doing?
And Oh my goodness that was brilliant,
That was absolutely brilliant,
He's dived through Spence's legs;
But he's got him,
This rugged stopper has him by the coat
And Rover's barking in there too;
He'll never get out of this one.
But this is unbelievable!
He's got away
He has got away:
He wriggled out of his coat
And left part of his trousers with Rover.
This boy is real dynamite.
He's over the wall
He's clear
They'll never catch him now.
He's down the yard and on his way
And I don't think we're going to see
Any more of Markey
Until it's safe to come home.

The New House

I don't much like this bedroom
The bedroom doesn't care for me
It looks at me like a policeman
Inspecting a refugee.

The bathroom doesn't feel like home at all
Feels more like an empty space,
And the mirror seems used to staring at
A completely different face.

I don't like the smell of the kitchen
Don't like the garden or the rain
Feels like a deserted station
Where I'm waiting for a train.

I can't kick a ball against this wall,
I can't build a house in this tree
And the streets are as quiet and deserted
As the local cemetery.

I don't like the look of the kids next door
Playing in the beat-up car
Why do they stand and stare at me?
Who do they think they are?

The big boy's coming over
He's just about my height
Why has he got a brick in his hand?
Is he going to pick a fight?

But he asks us into their garden
He tells us his name is Ben
And Jane is the name of his sister
And will we help them build their den.

We can't get it finished by dinner time
We won't get it finished by tea
But there'll be plenty of time in the days ahead
For Ben, Jane, Andy and me.

Street Cricket

On August evenings by the lamppost
When the days are long and light
The lads come out for cricket
And play until it's night.
They bat and bowl and field and shout
And someone shouts 'HOWZAT!'
But you can't give Peter Batty out
Or he'll take away his bat.

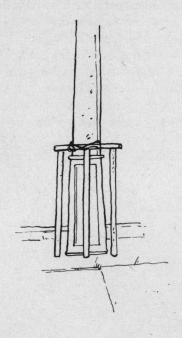

The dogs in the Close all love to field
And chase about the street
The stumper wears his mother's gloves
And stops the ball with his feet.
Everyone should have a bowl
That's the proper way to play
But Batty has to bowl all night
Or he takes his ball away.

When lamps and rooms turn on their lights
And you can hardly see the ball
The lads begin to drift off home
You can hear the goodbyes they call.
But Peter Batty's two hundred not out
And he shouts as he walks away,
'Remember I'm batting tomorrow night
Or I won't let anyone play.'

Half Asleep

Half asleep
And half awake
I drift like a boat
On an empty lake.
And the sounds in the house
And the street that I hear
Though far away sound very clear.
That's my sister Betty
Playing by the stairs
Shouting like teacher
At her teddy bears.
I can hear Mum chatting
To the woman next door
And the tumble drier
Vibrates through the floor.
That's Alan Simpson
Playing guitar
While his Dad keeps trying
To start their car.
Dave the mechanic
Who's out on strike
Keeps revving and tuning
His Yamaha bike.
From the open window
Across the street
On the August air
Drifts a reggae beat.
At four o'clock
With a whoop and a shout
The kids from St John's
Come tumbling out.
I can hear their voices
Hear what they say
And I play in my head
All the games that they play.

Bossy Queen Eileen

Out from under a dirty blanket
That she and Betty have slung
Between the rabbit hutch and next door's fence
Come the bossy specs of Bossy Eileen
Followed by her bossy nose
And the rest of her bossy face.
'Bet you'll never guess what we've built,'
Says Bossy Eileen
Tucking her skirt into her knickers
And doing handstands against the wall.
'Is it an Apache tent?' I suggest,
Knowing that whatever I say is bound to be wrong.
Bossy Eileen is just as bossy upside down
As she is the right way up.
'Course not clever clogs so there,'
Says her red upside-down face,
'Anyone can see it's a royal palace.'
Bossy Eileen comes the right way up.

29

'You must call me Queen Eileen
And your Royal Highness if you want to play,
And this is Princess Betty who's come for tea,'
She says tugging her frock out of her knickers.
'Thank you your majesty,' simpers Betty
Making her thin legs go buckled
And holding up the corners of her skirt.
'If you like,' says Queen Bossy Boots Eileen,
You can be King today,
Unless you'd rather be a humble footman?'
'No, king will do fine,' I tell her
Curtsying like Betty.
I find out that a king
Spends a lot of time
Bringing rain water in broken plastic cups
And crab apples to the royal tea party.
Betty spoons away at the dirt:
'You must give me the recipe for this junket,'
She says in her put-on voice.
The September afternoon is spent
Sweeping out the battlements,
Bowing to many guests
And rebuilding the royal palace
When the blanket falls in.
So passes
Another royal afternoon.

Bouncing

Sally Arkari isn't she a treat
Bouncing her rubber ball
Up and down the street
Sticking plaster spectacles
Braces on her teeth
Always scoffing chocolates
Always crunching sweets
Never stops bouncing
Wherever she goes
Never stops sniffing
Never blows her nose
She bounces when she's laughing
Shc bounces when she weeps
She bounces when she's wide awake
She bounces when she sleeps
She bounces in the playground
She bounces in the hall

You can always tell it's Sally
By her bouncing rubber ball
She bounces during Geography
She bounces during Art
She bounces all through dinner time
In the custard tart
She bounces 'till she's out of breath
And her face turns red
She bounces in assembly
On the teacher's head
She bounces to the fairground
And makes the people cross
As she bounces in the fish and chips
And in the candy floss
She bounces into Paris
And for almost an hour
She bounced her little rubber ball
On the Eiffel tower
She bounced down to the circus
And up the greasy pole
She bounced down to the football ground
And bounced into the goal
She bounced beside the brass band
As it marched around the town
She bounced among the drummer boys
And made them all fall down
She bounced it on her knee caps
She bounced it on her head
Then she bounced her way back home again
And bounced into her bed.

The Alchemist

There's a mysterious light
Burns all through the night
In that house where some people say
The alchemist dwells
With books full of spells
And a cat who scares children away.

Some say that he lives
In that house all alone
Some say he has claws and a beak
Some say he keeps rats
And vampire bats
And a raven he's taught how to speak.

And the children play dare:
'I dare you to spy
Through the dust on his window pane.'
They say those who dare
To enter his lair
Have never been seen again.

They say that his furnace
Turns iron and bronze
Into ingots of glistening gold.
They say if you take
The powder he makes
You'll never fall sick or grow old.

Some say he's a wizard
Some say he's a saint
Some say he eats toads for his tea
So I don't think I'll pay
Him a visit today
For fear he should want to eat me.

The Cat

Conscious of being a cat
I am given to sensuality.
I like to slide my bulk
Against the nylon ankles of young ladies,
Then again I fold my fur
On silken eiderdowns
And take pleasure in simply walking,
Turn up my nose at meat,
Disdain creamless milk
And fattened by the heat of open fires
Compose myself for sleep
Within the tidy limits of myself
Even in the best company.

The Bantam Cock

Before I cross the farm each day
I always hope and pray
That the green and crimson bantam cock
Won't be there to bar my way.

Oh bantam cock please let me pass
Let me cross your yard today
I beg you please don't charge at me
And make me run away.

Don't make your crop to stand on end
Don't crow your clarion pride
Don't flap your wings and stretch your throat
Don't spread your beak so wide.

I must go fishing in the river
I just have to cross your farm
I don't intend to steal your eggs
Or cause your chickens harm.

He struts stiff-legged up and down
Like a major on parade
His angry eyes both seem to say
I'm used to being obeyed.

And though I creep so silently
With my rod beneath my arm
He swivels his head and lifts his throat
And trumpets his alarm.

Now here he comes stiffly running
His head thrust out before
His furious crop streams above his head
Like a bloodstained flag of war.

I race across the muddy field
For the safety of the gate
While the scuttling bantam comes closer
On wings of pride and hate.

And just in time I'm safe and sound
And bang the farm gate to
And calmly inform my bristling foe,
'I'm not afraid of you.'

My Sister Betty

My sister Betty said,
'I'm going to be a famous actress.'
Last year she was going to be a missionary.
'Famous actresses always look unhappy but beautiful,'
She said, pulling her mouth sideways
And making her eyes turn upwards
So they were mostly white.
'Do I look unhappy but beautiful?'
'I want to go to bed and read,' I said.
'Famous actresses suffer and have hysterics,' she said.
'I've been practising my hysterics.'
She began going very red and screaming
So that it hurt my ears.
She hit herself on the head with her fists
And rolled off my bed on to the lino.
I stood by the wardrobe where it was safer.
She got up saying, 'Thank you, thank you,'
And bowed to the four corners of my bedroom.
'Would you like an encore of hysterics?' she asked.
'No,' I said from inside the wardrobe.
There was fluff all over her vest.
'If you don't clap enthusiastically,' she said,
'I'll put your light out when you're reading.'
While I clapped a bit
She bowed and shouted, 'More, more!'
Auntie Gwladys shouted upstairs,
'Go to bed and stop teasing our Betty.'
'The best thing about being a famous actress,' Betty said,
'Is that you get to die a lot.'
She fell to the floor with a crash
And lay there for an hour and a half
With her eyes staring at the ceiling.

She only went away when I said,
'You really look like a famous actress
Who's unhappy but beautiful.'

When I got into bed and started reading,
She came and switched off my light.
It's not much fun
Having a famous actress for a sister.

Death of a Gunfighter

Doc Holliday, who are you waiting for
With your fevered eyes alive?
Why do your hands feed cartridges
Into your pearl-handled forty-five?

Doc Holliday, why do you cock an ear
To the hoof beats pattering by?
Who is the stranger on a jet black mare
With death in either eye?

The room throbs like an oven,
The sun climbs up to noon,
The stranger sways in the rocking chair
Outside the Last Chance Saloon.

Doc Holliday asks for a mirror
No reflection in the glass
Only the ghosts of the men he's killed
Smiling as they pass.

The Pinkerton man in Ellsworth
When you were running from the law,
The kid in Dodge out to make his name
By beating you to the draw.

The breed in Butte, Montana,
Who marked you with that scar,
The dude who marked you with a slug in your thigh
From a face out in Wichita.

You can't be searching for glory now
For eternity in the sun
But hoping to find a kind of peace
In the mouth of a stranger's gun.

Doc Holliday white as the sheet on his bed,
The room about him reeled,
Coughed in his white bandanna
Stained like a poppy field.

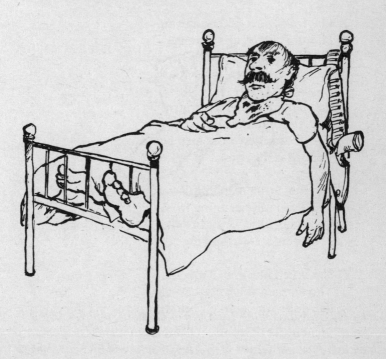

The stranger sits quiet at the bedside
Watching the life blood spill
Doc's hands reach out for unseen guns
Then slowly flutter still.

The gun belt hangs on the bed post
The hat on a hook on the wall
And the high-heeled boots he'll never wear
Stand polished in the hall.

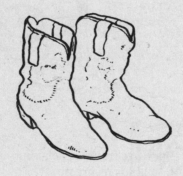

*(Doc Holliday died of tuberculosis in a sanatorium in Glenwood
Springs at the age of thirty-five. On his death bed he is reputed to
have asked for a last drink of whiskey, then raised his head, looked
down at his feet and whispered, 'Well I'll be damned.'
Doc had always sworn that he would die with his boots on.)*

42

The Cisco Kid of Cable Street

Down the long dry canyons he rides
Past arroyas and arid gulches lined with mesquite,
Through winding wheels of tumbleweed
Whipped by the hot winds of the sierras
To where amongst the stables
And the clapboard stores
Fate waits for him darkly with feet astride;
Fate who smiles bitterly
And somewhere reserves
A bullet just for him.
Hunched in the saddle
The Kid sings softly
A song about himself and his fame.

> *'I'm the Cisco Kid of Cable Street,*
> *My hand moves fast as light.*
> *In the high noon sun*
> *I draw my gun*
> *Fast as a rattler's bite.'*

At the saloon he swings from his palamino,
The hot afternoon holds its breath.
His cool eyes take in the mayor,
The quailing townsfolk froze in time and fear.
On the threshold of the saloon
He stands motionless;
The hands over the cards hold still
The faro wheel revolves unwatched
The bartender freezes
Amongst the bourbon and the sarsaparilla
His cigar halfway to his lips.

Hands hooked loose over his pearl-handled guns
The Kid walks into his own legend.
'There's your order,'
Says the man behind the counter.
'Tell your mother there's no brown bread today.'
And smiling he hands over the change.
They know not to mess about with the Kid.

Horror Film

Well sir, first of all there was this monster
But like he's not really a monster
'Cause in real life he's a bank clerk sir
And sings in this village choir
But he keeps like drinking this potion sir
And you see him like changing into this pig
With black curly hairs on its knuckles;
And what he does sir,
Is he goes round eating people's brains.
Anyway before that sir, I should have said
He's secretly in love with Lady Irene
Who's very rich with lots of long frocks
And she has this identical twin sister
Who looks like her sir
Who keeps getting chased by this monster bulldog
Into these sinking sands
That's inhabited by this prehistoric squid sir
Which like she can't see
Because the deaf and dumb bailiff
With the hump on his back
Has trod on her specs.
Anyway before that sir,
I should have said,
This lady Irene is screaming,
'Henry, Henry, my beloved, save me,'
'Cause she's been walled up in the dripping dungeon
With the mad violinist of the vaults
By the manservant with the withered boot sir.
But this Henry, he can't hear her sir,
Because he's too busy
Putting people in this bubbling acid bath
To make them stay young forever sir
But his experiments keep going wrong.

Anyway, before that sir,
I should have said,
Her Dad can't rescue her either sir
Because of the army of giant ants
That's eating his castle;
And the music sir, it's going,
'Tarrar, tarrar, boom boom tarrar sir,'
And 'Henry, Henry my beloved,'
She keeps screaming
And the mad violinist of the vaults sir
He starts going funny all over the flagstones.
And like, Algernon sir,
No not him sir, the other one,
He can't do nothing about the squid in the bogs
Because he's turning into this pig with hairy knuckles.
Anyway before that sir, I should have said,
There's this huge mummy in the library
And every time he hears this music
Starts tearing off all these dirty bandages
And smashing through these walls and everything
And the professor can't stop him
'Cause he's gone off his rocker
And keeps bulging his eyes and laughing a lot
When suddenly this vampire . . .
Didn't I tell you about the vampire sir?
Anyway before that there's this vampire
Who's been dead for thousands of years
But he's a Swiss greengrocer in real life
But the iceberg his coffin's in
Gets all broken up sir
When it collides with Dr Strenkhoff's submarine sir,
That's carrying this secret cargo
Of radio active rats . . .
Didn't I tell you about the radio active rats sir?
Well anyway sir
Before that I should have said . . .

Invalid

Such a commotion
Coming up off the street,
Such a shouting and calling
Such a running of feet.
Such a rolling of marbles
Such a whipping of tops
Such a skipping of skips
Such a hopping of hops –
And I'm in bed.

So much chasing and fighting
Down on the street
Such a claiming of victories
Such howling defeats.
So much punching and shoving
So much threatening to clout
So much running to doorways
Until it's safe to come out –
But I'm in bed.

So much hiding and seeking
From the pavement below
So much argy bargy
Who'll hide and whose go.
Such a throwing of balls
Such picking of sides
Such a racing of bikes
Such a begging of rides –
And I'm in bed.

If I was a dictator
And the world was a street
There'd be no more homework
No school dinners to eat.
I'd abolish exams
I'd banish all sums
And we'd play in a street
Where night never comes –
And I'd never be ill.

Anna Mae 'Chip Shop' O'Sullivan

Anna Mae Chip Shop O'Sullivan
Ran a shop from a Dormobile van.
Served cod wrapped in last week's Beano
Had a chin like Desperate Dan.

Anna Mae Beano O'Sullivan
Built like a battleship
Smoked a pipe like a skull and cross bones
And talked like a comic strip.

She'd say:

JOKE COW PIE FOR THE BASH STREET KIDS
YUK, SPLUTTER, CHOMP AND SPLAT!
GRRR, RAGE, IT'S THAT TOFF LORD SNOOTY
WANTING SPRATS FOR KORKY THE CAT

Thinks:

> THIS SNEEZING SALT SHOULD IMPROVE THE FLAVOUR
> ADD SUPERGLUE FLAVOUR FOR FUN
> HOHO, CHORTLE CHORTLE WHEN SNITCH AND SNATCH
> SCOFF THIS MAGIC EXPLODING BUN.

Moans:

> GROAN, YUK IT'S THAT DENIS THE MENACE
> EEEK AND WITH GNASHER THE DOG
> OH GLEE THEY'RE SCOFFING THAT HAMBURGER
> STUFFED WITH A YUMMY PLASTIC FROG.

Anna Mae Chip Shop O'Sullivan
Her van wasn't there one day
They said she'd hadn't a licence
So the council towed her away.

Anna Mae Long Gone O'Sullivan
Your legend won't die though you're gone
You're stored in our dreams like a comic strip
Whose story goes on and on
And on and on
And on

And on

And on

50

And on

A Dog's Life

Waking up last Friday and dressing for school
I found I'd turned into a dog.
I looked at myself in the glass.
Same Ben with glasses and broken tooth stared back
But I just knew I was an alsatian.
'You're an alsatian,' I said to my reflection.
'Woof woof,' my reflection barked back.
No doubt about it, I was an alsatian.
I rushed into the bathroom
Where my sister was cleaning her teeth.
'I'm an alsatian,' I barked happily,
'My name's Attila.'
'Stop being stupid,' she said. 'I'm late for school.'
I sank my teeth into this piece of leg
That came out of a nightie.
'Good dog Attila,' she agreed.

I chased downstairs on all fours
Barking joyfully;
Being an alsatian called Attila agreed with me.
My new life came as a surprise to my mother
Since I have two sisters, a brother and a father
And not one of them is an alsatian.
'Good morning,' I barked to my mother and father
Giving a big grin and letting my tongue loll out.
'I'm an alsatian,' I said,
Standing on my back legs on the chair
And resting my paws in the All Bran.
'Stop dribbling and eat your breakfast properly,'
Said my mother.
'Woof woof,' I explained from my place under the sofa
Trying to eat a sausage without using my front paws.
'Your son's an alsatian,' said my mother.
'Dr McEever said we might see a sudden improvement,'
Said my father from behind his newspaper.
After the first shock, they soon got used to the idea
Of having a dog with spectacles called Attila
About the house;
Parents can be very adaptable
If you give them a chance.
It's a good life now,
A dog's life.

There's less homework, I don't have to shut doors
And I have my own place on a mat by the fire.
I spend my days sniffing and looking purposeful.
Some days I bury motor bikes
Or bits of sideboard in the cabbage patch.
Baby Sophie likes me a lot;
She gurgles and chuckles as I lick her face
Or try to herd the tortoise into her playpen
Suddenly I feel wanted.
My family speak to me a lot now
And are learning what my barks mean.
'Good boy Attila,' they say and tickle my ears.
My father spends hours taking me for walks
Or throwing sticks for me to bring back in my jaws.
And then to hear my mother calling
On some sunlit afternoon,
'Attila, Attila, time for cubs.'
And I romp up from the garden my tail wagging,
Weaving between the apple trees
And the white sheets on the line.
Well, there's nothing like it.
You really should try it sometime.

Arthur the Fat Boy

They said about Arthur
You're too fat
They said you can never win,
Only make a fool of yourself,
They said: Arthur think again.

But Arthur was sick of the insults
He was tired of all the names
He was fed up with never being asked to play
When they picked the teams for games.

So secretly he went running
In the evenings after tea
Past the allotments down to the old canal
Where he thought no one would see.

And there each night Arthur ran alone
Till his fat pink legs were numb
And the sweat on his face was a river
And his lungs beat like a drum.

He ran past locks and bridges
Where abandoned factories reared
Where the wind on the water called his name
And only the silence jeered.

Then finally sports day came around
And Arthur jogged to his place
And the mocking shouts of the jeering crowd
Made the tears course down his face.

But the jeers and the laughter died away
When the starter fired his gun
And a voice rang clear across the field:
Just look at that fat boy run.

Two laps from home and Arthur lies fourth
There's a map of pain on his face
And only his rage keeps him running
As he moves up into third place.

He inches up on the second boy
The leader's just ten yards ahead
And the voice of the crowd is a roar in his head
And the faces a sea of red.

And Arthur the fat boy sees the tape
And his pride has become a mine
And he scratches with his will for strength there
As his legs swim for the line.

And Arthur the fat boy makes first place
But the sky is upside down
And the finish appears to be moving away
As he falls to his knees on the ground.

He can hear the second boy closing fast
But his legs have turned to lead
And his brain can't hear his will power scream
Through the blizzard in his head.

And though for the first time in his life
He hears the crowd call his name
Arthur lies stranded high and alone
Beached on a rack of pain.

Then a mocking voice rings high and clear
It's a voice he's heard all his life
And the jeering, leering mockery
Twists in his heart like a knife.

And it's anger that sets him moving
Anger that lifts him again
It's anger that pushes his aching legs
Crawling across the line.

And Arthur the fat boy dreams he's in bed
And he clings to his dream in fear
So many cold mornings he's woken to see
His happiness disappear,

And Arthur reluctantly wakens himself
And the world turns like a wheel
And Arthur for the first time in his life
Awakes to a dream that's real.

Christmas Morning

On Christmas mornings
I wake up to see
What Father Christmas
Has brought for me.
Wrapped in my blanket
Like a cocoon
I wonder if this time
I've woken too soon.
Perhaps my stocking
Of blue and white
Will still be as empty
As it was last night.
Is it too early to take a peep?
But I'm too excited
To go back to sleep.
I crawl in the dark
To the foot of the bed
My heart bumping softly
With excitement and dread.
And yes! He's been,
There can be no doubt
The stocking's all bulges
When my hand reaches out.
When my family crowd shouting
In through my door
I know that Christmas
Has come round once more.

Sally won't you walk with me?

'Sally won't you walk with me
Walking heel and toe
Sally can we secrets share
As home from school we go.'

Arm in arm by lane and hedge
So many tales to tell
And every tale breeds tales anew
As we walk in a magic spell.

'And do you know what Brenda said
And how Alan banged his head
How Antonia cried at dinner time
And what Jemima said?'

'And wasn't dinner awful?
And Sally tell your dream
And will you come to tea next week?
And isn't Rose a scream?'

'Did you really tell your mother that
Did your sister cut your hair
Did you see that lady on the bike
Did you see those two boys stare?'

'And Sally look, stop giggling
Oh Sally honestly
Oh Sally don't you pull that face
Those people there will see.'

'What did your father say to that
And did you do it again?
You didn't really, I don't believe!
Sally what happened then?'

We whisper over Sally's gate
Till her mother calls her to tea
So many secrets still to tell
So many tales about me.

And if I could wish my days again
If time were a golden spool
I'd wish I could walk for ever
With Sally home from school.

Salcombe (1948)

Oh I remember how the sea
Came washing to our feet
That morning
And how my mother chanced to meet
Your mother
And father dozed in the August heat
And the gulls cried.

And how you said your name was Anne
And how my sister teased
Your cousin
And how your dog played as he pleased
In the waves
And barked and shook himself and sneezed
And the band played

And how amongst the parasols and feet
We dug beneath the strand
A tunnel
And how my fingers wet with sand
Suddenly
Broke through and touched your stranger's hand
And the world turned.

The Pain

Coming home from school when I was seven
I told my mother of the pain.
'Where is the pain?' she asked.
'Here,' I said, holding before me
Two imaginary pillows in the air.
'Where were you when it started?'
'At Farnborough Road Juniors
But then I took it on the bus with me.'
'At what time did the pain start?'
'Between the end of dinner time
And the ringing of the bell for afternoon.'
'Was it something you ate? How did you notice it?'
'It walked through the door of Miss Mellor's class.
Before there was just me
Afterwards there were two of us,
The pain and me.'
'Was anything said? Did anybody notice?'
'Something was said about the register.
When the room was empty
The pain had made its home there.'
'Can't you tell me more?' my mother said.
She was getting bored with the conversation.
'What would you call the pain?'
'The pain is called Nancy Muriel Oliver
And is pale with yellow hair.
Is there nothing you can do,
Nothing you can say?'
'No,' said my mother,
Closing the medicine cabinet.
'Just go back to school tomorrow
And pray it never goes away.'

Invisible

It wasn't a sudden thing;
There were no falling stars
Or choirs of voices,
No rushes of wind
Or flashes of lightning –
I simply woke up one morning
And wasn't there.
Or at least,
I knew I was there
But there wasn't anything to be seen
That you might have called me.
If anybody had been there they would have seen
A huge smile of pride creasing my face,
That is if I had a face
For a smile to crease on.
It hadn't been easy;
Every day for nearly a year
I'd been trying to persuade my body
To have second thoughts
About being there.
In quiet corners unobserved
I'd order my body
To go away.
'Go away body,' I'd say
But my body seemed to need more convincing.
Down I'd look
And there it would still be,
Being there, all over the place.
I had a very stubborn body
Where being there was concerned.
But now all that effort
Seemed to be worthwhile.

I'm not saying I didn't have
Little doubts.
For example I said to myself,
'If you're not there anymore
Where are you?'
Or to put it another way,
How could I know
I wasn't there
If I wasn't there
To know that I wasn't.
After a bit
All this thinking
Started to make my head ache,
That is if I'd had a head
To make aches with.
I got up out of bed;
Put my clothes on my invisible body;
Washed my invisible face;
Brushed my invisible teeth
And took my invisible self on a walk
To meet the world.
It would be a day to remember
I promised myself.
What fun, I thought,
I'll have with my sister,
The postman,
The school librarian
And my haughty teacher with the spectacles
Miss Simpkins.
But
Although I told them
I was invisible
Nobody would believe
What they couldn't see
In front of their own eyes.

When the jug poured milk
As if by magic,
Instead of falling down
Into a faint with amazement
My sister said,
'You'll be late for school.'
The gate was pushed open
By an unseen hand;
But the postman only said,
'Two letters for you.'
Books flew unaided into the shelves;
'What a helpful boy,'
Said the librarian.
Spellings wrote themselves
Across my exercise book;
'Could do better,'
Wrote Miss Simpkins
In haughty red handwriting.
When I shouted at them all,
'I'm invisible,
I'm invisible,
Look at me, I'm invisible!'
They all smiled
The same tight-lipped smile.
They don't know
That they can't see me.

Christmas at our House

The Christmases at our house
Aren't like the pictures I've seen
On calendars and Christmas cards
Where all is joy serene,
Where red-faced husbands kiss their wives
Beneath sprigs of mistletoe
And fat little angels sing carols
And it always seems to snow.
For a start my Dad starts moaning
Before he's even out of bed
And Elvis, my brother, starts screaming
When his Action Man loses his head.
And Ann won't touch her turkey
And Elvis starts calling her names
And Dad overdoes the brandy
And the pudding bursts into flames.
Auntie May starts singing long, sad hymns
And the mongrel is sick on the mat
While Uncle George gets merry
On just three glasses of sherry
And spills custard all over the cat.
After tea we play disorganized games
And Gran faints away in her chair
And the games always end in tears and sulks
Because Elvis will never play fair.
Sharron falls out with her boyfriend,
Tina stops talking to hers,
Then we have to call the fire brigade
When Tom's head gets stuck in the stairs.
I breathe a sigh of relief when midnight arrives
And the relations all disappear
Because I know for certain that Christmas Day
Won't be round for another whole year.

Growing up

I know a lad called Billy
Who goes along with me
He plays this game
Where he uses my name
And makes people think that he's me.

Don't ever mess with Billy
He's a vicious sort of bloke
He'll give you a clout
For saying nowt
And thump you for a joke.

My family can't stand Billy
Can't bear him round the place
He won't eat his food
He's rough and rude
And wears scowls all over his face.

No one can ever break Billy
He's got this look in his eye
That seems to say
You can wale me all day
But you'll not make Billy cry.

He has a crazy face has Billy
Eyes that look but can't see
A mouth like a latch
Ears that don't match
And a space where his brain should be.

Mad Billy left one morning
Crept away without being seen
Left his body for me
That fits perfectly
And a calm where his madness had been.

Mandy likes the Mud

Polly likes to play with toys
Melissa makes a lot of noise
Ann has a bike
Trevor a trike
But Mandy likes the mud.
She jumps in it
She slumps in it
She scoops it in her hands
She rides on it
She slides on it
She digs to foreign lands.

Kevan likes to kick a ball
Peter never plays at all
Tina cooks tarts
Donna plays darts
But Mandy loves the mud.
She galumphs in it
She splarges
She glugs and slurps and slops
She grins in it
She swims in it
She does smacking belly flops.

Tricia talks to her teddy bear
Belinda combs her doll's long hair
Tracy plays tennis
Mark is a menace
But Mandy adores the mud.
She dives in it
She thrives in it
She paints it on the wall

She goes splash in it
She goes splosh in it
She does the breast stroke and the crawl.

Ronnie likes falling
And snowballing in snow
Lucy is learning how to row
Louise loves a sing-song
Paula likes ping-pong
But Mandy rejoices in mud.
She has sat in it
Filled her hat with it
She washed the neighbour's cat in it
She hid from Mum in it
Banged her drum in it
She fell down on her bum in it.

Kenneth kicks an old tin can
Anthony plays with his Action Man
Wanda is waiting
For Sam to go skating
But Mandy lives in the mud.
So if you're looking for Mandy
Find the muddiest mess
At Mud House, Mud Corner
Her permanent muddress.

The Building Site

In a haze of brick dust
And red sun
All day long the men slog,
Lumbering about
The churned ridges of clay
In clod-hopping boots,
Humping great hods
On the brawn of red shoulders
Up piped and rattling scaffolds
And uneven boards
To where their mates
With deft flicks from trowels
Make house walls grow
Brick by red brick.
All day too
The great trucks bang and clatter
Back and forth
And the churning mixer
Slops out gobs of concrete
In wholesome pats
On to the dusty earth.

At twelve
They break off
And swarm from scaffolding
To drink brown tea
From huge mugs
That they grip in the beef of their fists.
After, they kick a ball about
Or lie and bronzy in the sun
Until it's turn-to time again.

The afternoon shift wears on;
They whistle more,
Shout and laugh
And sing the songs
That blare from two transistors.
At six they knock off
And pack into a lorry
With their clobber.
Down the rutted track they bound
Shouting and cheering.
When the pandemonium clears,
The shells of houses stand
Workmanless, untenanted and still.
Silence in the settling haze.
A sparrow bounces on rubble,
A curious mongrel snuffles
On a tail-wagging inspection tour,
Finds it good
And departs for an important meeting.
I wouldn't mind being a labourer
For a bit.

The Vandalingo

In the rotting lake called Albion
That's thick as kedgeree
Lurks the odious Vandalingo
With his scurvy wife Debris.

Beneath a mildewed, rusting gas fire
Near an old bike and a plank
The Vandalingo makes his home
In a waste disposal tank.

His carcass smells of Wellingtons
His boots are size fifteen
His nails leak inky messages
To his baby son Globscene.

His teeth are broken hacksaw blades
His lips drip kerosene
He belches fumes and poison gas
From his lungs of polythene.

For years he sleeps his dreamless sleeps
Amongst rusting beds and cars
But then one night he rises up
To sport beneath the stars.

And then through webs of rotting weeds
Two spinning fog lamps loom
As the Vandalingo's yellow eyes
Peer dimly through the gloom.

The surface of the rotting lake
Lifts like a tent of slime
As the Vandalingo crashes through
To chant his ancient rhyme.

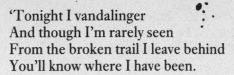

'Tonight I vandalinger
And though I'm rarely seen
From the broken trail I leave behind
You'll know where I have been.

'I crash through walls and hedges
I uproot flowers and trees
I spread garbage, swill and bacon rind
Where they're sure to cause disease.

'I scrawl my name on subway walls
I chew the seats on trains
I hurl prams and bottles into ponds
And my head through window panes.'

And if your school's been flooded
And there's ink down every wall
You can be sure that sometime in the night
The Vandalingo's called.

As dawn creeps up the city streets
He drags home 'neath the moon's pale stare
And in a belch of bubbling mud
Sinks gurgling to his lair.

And there he's joyfully welcomed
By Globscene and his spouse Debris
And to the waking world above
They wail this song of glee.

'We are the Vandalingos
There's but one thought in our brain
That though we sleep ten thousand years
Our time will come again.'

The Old Man of Wells

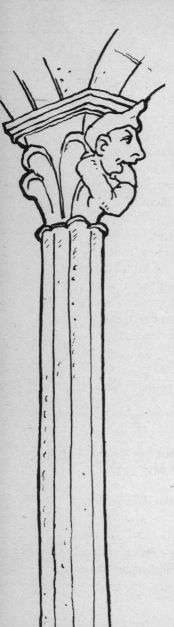

Here sit I
Glum and alone
Stuck on my column
Of freezing stone,
Here crouch I
The Old Man of Wells
Battered and deafened
By the clatter of bells.
Eternal eyes
Gazing South
Eternal finger
In eternal mouth.
Rubbing my tooth
In rain and sleet
While uncaring centuries
Crawl 'neath my feet.
Saint Appolina
To you I pray
Make a miracle take
My pain away.
But he has no pity
On my pain
Only the West Wind
Hears me complain.
Why put *me* here
In this holy place
With my wine-jug ears
And gormless face.
Raised in a byre
With two pigs and a hen
Now my neighbours are holy men.

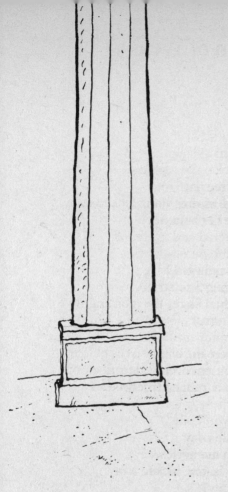

'There's your gargoyle,'
I heard the Abbot shout,
'Stick a pipe in his mouth
For the rain to spill out.'
The poor can't argue
With the likes of he,
If he wants a gargoyle
That's what I'll be.
So kind mortals
Who stand and stare
Consider my tooth
When you kneel in prayer.
Pray that this wound
In my tooth may mend
And that like this poem
The pain will end.

On a pillar in Wells Cathedral is the effigy of a peasant who suffers agonies of toothache and rubs the bad tooth with his finger.

Saint Appolina is the patron saint of those who suffer from the toothache.

A gargoyle is a figure, usually grotesque, either man or animal or a mixture of both who has a spout in his mouth in order to carry rain water clear of the Cathedral wall.

77

Wedding Day

Lillian McEever is bride for the day
Wearing Mummy's old wedding dress long locked away
And a posy of dandelions for her bouquet
And a tiara of daisies.

Birdsong showers silver on Institute Drive
Where Lillian waits for her guests to arrive
And the shouts and the laughter shake the morning alive
There's a wedding today.

Past the brook they wind where the cherry trees bloom
Casting white showers of blossom over bride and groom
And grandmothers dream in curtained front rooms
And remember.

Lillian McEever forget not this day
For Spring mornings die but memories stay
When the past like the dress is long locked away
And the leaves fall.

Skipping Song

Ann and Belinda
Turning the rope
Helen jumps in
But she hasn't got a hope
Helen Freckles
What will you do
Skip on the table
In the Irish stew
Freckles on her face
Freckles on her nose
Freckles on her bum
Freckles on her toes
Helen Freckles
Tell me true
How many freckles
Have you got on you
One two three four five six seven
And out goes you.

Stella Starwars
Skip in soon
Into your spaceship
And off to the moon
Skip on the pavement
One and two

Skip like a rabbit
Or a kangaroo
Skip so high
You never come down
Over the steeples
Over the town
Skip over rooftops
Skip over trees
Skip over rivers
Skip over seas
Skip over London
Skip over Rome
Skip all night
And never come home
Skip over moonbeams
Skip over Mars
Skip through the Milky Way
And try to count the stars
One two three four five six seven
Out goes you.

Space Shot

Out of the furnace
The great fish rose
Its silver tail on fire
But with a slowness
Like something sorry
To be rid of earth.
The boiling mountains
Of snow white cloud
Searched for a space to go into
And the ground thundered
With a roar
That set teacups
Rattling in a kitchen
Twenty miles away.
Across the blue it arched
Milk bottle white
But shimmering in the haze.
And the watchers by the fence
Held tinted glass against their eyes
And wondered at what man could do
To make so large a thing
To fly so far and free.
While the unknown Universe waited;
For waiting
Was what it had always been good at.

Moonscape 2400

With each dawning
The older colonists
Who had arrived in the first ships
During the Summer 2320
Settle themselves
Into the Viewing Quadrant
To watch the Earth rise
Like a blackened marble.
Their eyes expressionless,
They make a picture of
How it was
Creep into their minds.
Master control cannot see this
And anyway the men
Are too old to be dangerous.
The third generation
Call out each other's numbers
And crowd about the flashing boxes
In the Electro Pleasure Dome.
In the dust beyond the city
Coca-cola tins fill the craters
And one boy is slapped
For asking what memory is.

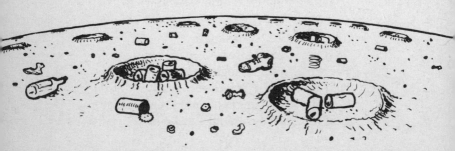

Lessons in History

After three orbits
Of the unknown planet
The multi-spectral scanner
Showed vegetation
But no other life.
When we told Command
That we were going in,
We felt their excitement
Through the stream of data;
The benefits of colonization
Were apparent to us all.
They left the descent decision to us
And wished us every kind of luck.
The logic bank was reassuring:
— REMEMBER ALWAYS YOU ARE MEN.
— HISTORY HAS ALWAYS PROVED
THE SUPERIORITY OF EXPLORERS.
— THEY MUST BE YOUR INFERIORS
OR THEY WOULD HAVE FOUND YOU FIRST.
We powered the retros and descended.
The jungle smothered us
In heat and darkness
But to the east a bloom of light
And in the light a rumbling
That one of us remarked
Was like a voice.
Moving forward
The light became a square
And the voice clearer.
We thought of the logic bank
And advanced, our weapons ready.
Somehow the square of light grew smaller
And we filled it with our heads.

The four of us peered out
Into something like a hall
With many people watching us.
We heard the historian say,
'And so two thousand years ago
Our forefathers arrived,'
Before his hand moved
Towards the off switch.

Message Understood

The Scantext stutters
'ALERT' in my brain.
I await further instructions.
The message comes through.
'SOLUTION CONCERNING THE ROBOTS.'
This has been expected.
I await further instructions.
My personal robot tries to read
The message in my brain
But my hypocrisy defeats him.
He smiles back at my false smile.
In many ways he is almost human.
The message is absorbed.
'THE ROBOTS HAVE OUTLIVED THEIR USE.
THEIR AMBITION THREATENS US.'
I await further instructions.
'LAST WEEK THREE OF THEM
WERE SEEN DANCING AND SINGING
IN THE DESERTED BALLROOM.'

I await further instructions.
'IF EACH HUMAN PLAYS HIS PART
THEN NO ONE WILL BE GUILTY.'
Message understood.
I prime my hand laser.
My robot turns to me
With something in his face
That in a man you might call fear.
For three seconds I squeeze the trigger.
The fine rod of light penetrates him.
He falls to the ground
His eyes turning to water.
Something like a song
Invades his throat
And his mouth leaks red.
Soon the threat will be over
If all humans do their duty.
Humming to myself
I await further instructions.

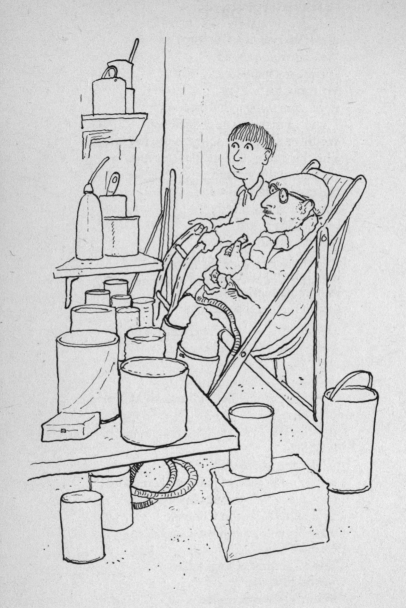

Shed in Space

My Grandad Lewis
On my mother's side
Had two ambitions.
One was to take first prize
For shallots at the village show
And the second
Was to be a space commander.
Every Tuesday
After I'd got their messages,
He'd lead me with a wink
To his garden shed
And there, amongst the linseed
And the sacks of peat and horse manure
He'd light his pipe
And settle in his deck chair.
His old eyes on the blue and distant
That no one else could see,
He'd ask,
'Are we A O.K. for lift off?'
Gripping the handles of the lawn mower
I'd reply:
'A O.K.'
And then
Facing the workbench,
In front of shelves of paint and creosote
And racks of glistening chisels.
He'd talk to Mission Control.
'Five-Four-Three-Two-One-Zero –
We have lift off.
This is Grandad Lewis talking,
Do you read me?
Britain's first space shed

is rising majestically into orbit
From its launch pad
In the allotments
In Lakey Lane.'

And so we'd fly,
Through timeless afternoons
Till tea time came,
Amongst the planets
And mysterious suns,
While the world
Receded like a dream:
Grandad never won
That prize for shallots,
But as the captain
Of an intergalactic shed
There was no one to touch him.

Johnny come over the Pasture

Johnny come over the pasture
Where the corn waves like the sea
Johnny come race me to the moon
Before we go home for tea.

Climb up here beside me
We'll ride on the old farm gate
We must reach the moon by five o'clock
Or else we'll be too late.

There's banana sandwiches and beans
And salmon paste and spam
And three sorts of jelly to fill your belly
And cake with marzipan.

Johnny the moon grows larger
But mother's calling me
Let's leave the moon until later
After we've both had tea.

Magdalena

By Lakey Lane allotments
Past the stream near Batty's Farm
Past the Laundry I go running
With Magdalena 'neath my arm.

Magdalena is a wonder
Her sails gleam purest white,
Her hull's the hue of a skylark's egg
She moves like an eagle's flight.

Magdalena on the water
Magdalena ship serene
Magdalena riding on the wind
Like a schooner in a dream.

And on certain Summer mornings
When no one else's near
I lay my head upon the grass
And through half-closed eyes I peer!

At Magdalena smoothly gliding
And her wake is like a sigh
And her sails tower white and billowing
Against the arched blue of the sky.

And the soft breeze on the water
Brings to me gently winging
The creak of a ghostly windlass
And long dead voices singing.

Six Views of a Waterfall

When the river threw itself off the cliff
It spun a twist of rope
So as not to lose touch with itself.

The river of a sudden
Tired of lying down between fields
And having the sky painted on its face
Stood up and was pleased.

Around the holy water where the miracle happened
They hollowed out a damp chapel
And glued green carpets on the wall to absorb the sound.
Every day someone brings fresh ferns.

We can see the silent film through the beaded curtain
There is interference on the vertical hold
And for a comedy there should be subtitles,
But the actors shout just the same.

Sometimes the river stays still
And children swim upstream.
After a time they lie down and walk away.

At home they have sardines for tea
And later go to bed.
While this is going on
The waterfall does what it has always done
And doesn't dream about people.

Song of the City

My brain is stiff with concrete
My limbs are rods of steel
My belly's stuffed with money
My soul was bought in a deal.

They poured metal through my arteries
They choked my lungs with lead
They churned my blood to plastic
They put murder into my head.

I'd a face like a map of the weather
Flesh that grew to the bone
But they tore my story out of my eyes
And turned my heart to stone.

Let me wind from my source like a river
Let me grow like wheat from the grain
Let me hold out my arms like a natural tree
Let my children love me again.